Stroma Yoles

Text based on M. Litt Dissertation
(St Andrews University, 1999)
Copy in Orkney Library
© Alastair R. Walker 2004
Photographs © various contributors

First published 2004 by
The Orcadian
Kirkwall
Orkney

Edited by Pamela Beasant

Printed by The Orcadian Limited
Hell's Half Acre, Hatston,
Kirkwall, Orkney.
KW15 1DW

ISBN 1-902957-22-9

Stroma Yoles

by
Alastair R. Walker

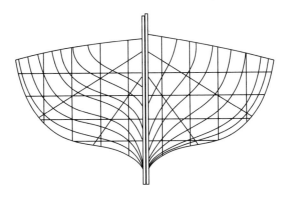

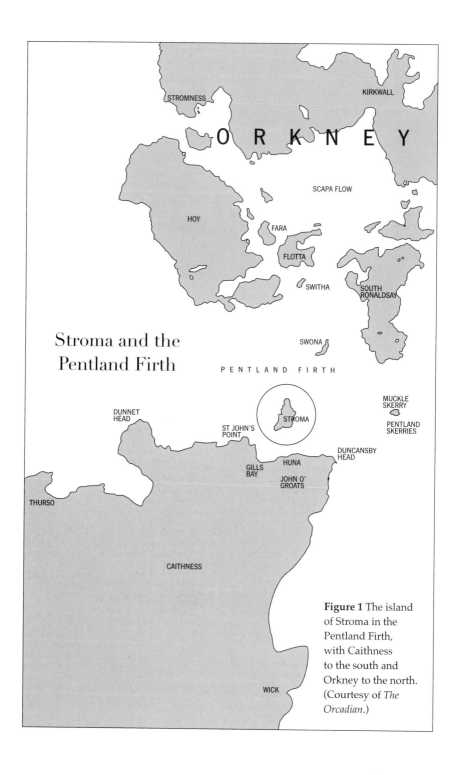

Stroma and the
Pentland Firth

Figure 1 The island of Stroma in the Pentland Firth, with Caithness to the south and Orkney to the north. (Courtesy of *The Orcadian*.)

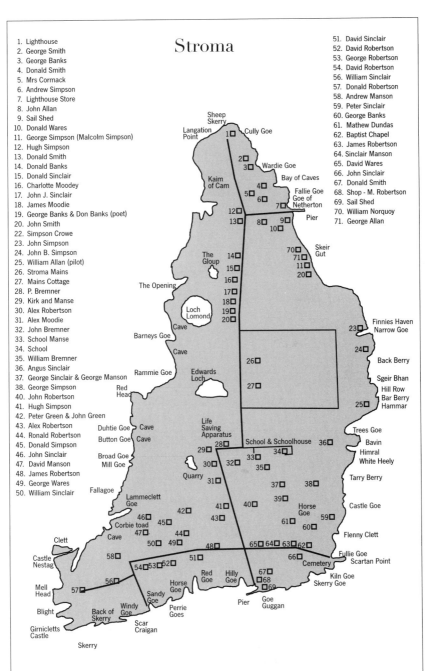

Figure 2 The island of Stroma. (Courtesy of Mr A.J. Sutherland and the Last House Museum, John O'Groats.)

Dedicated to
my wife Joanne
and my Mum and Dad

Acknowledgements

Very grateful thanks is given to all the people who
gave of their time and effort in providing information
for this project.

Particular thanks go to the people whose interviews
were recorded on tape, namely, William Mowatt,
Alex Annal, Iain Sutherland, Malcolm Simpson,
George Gunn, Peter Sinclair and Peter Matheson.
Thank you to all who showed me their yoles and to
James Simpson who took me across to the island
of Stroma.
In addition, many thanks to Pam Beasant who helped
prepare the text for publication.
Thank you to Len Wilson whose comments
on the text were very welcome.

Contents

Figures & Plates

Introduction

Very little has been written about the building of yoles on the island of Stroma, which lies to the north of mainland Scotland. What does exist is mentioned in a few books: *Stroma*, by D. Young; *Lest we forget the Parish of Canisbay*, by A.L. Houston; *Fishing the coastal tradition*, by M. Marshall; and in an unpublished thesis, *Boats in Medieval Orkney*, by A. Bowman. There was great opportunity for research in this field, especially as there are a number of people living in Orkney and Caithness who know a great deal about Stroma yoles. Invaluable opportunities for research also lay with some people who had been born and brought up on Stroma and whose forebears had built the yoles.

I set out to discover what constitutes a Stroma yole; where the design of the yoles originated; who built them and when. Since the Stroma yoles were operating on the Pentland Firth, research was done to find out the specific design features that were built into them to cope with the sea conditions there. The yoles were used for a variety of purposes by the community on Stroma, which I investigated.

I also wanted to find out if the people of Stroma made models of their boats.

One of the primary aims was to research in detail the way in which Stroma yoles were built. This included finding the location of the boatbuilding sites on Stroma, the origin of the boatbuilding materials and the type of tools used in the construction process. I also wanted to record the order in which the timbers were attached together to construct the yoles and the types of fastenings used, as well as the different features that completed the construction of the Stroma yoles. A lines drawing of a Stroma yole, *Superb*, (plate 23), helps to illustrate points throughout the book, as well as providing a plan for future replicas. (The name *Superb* is uncertain, another possibility is *Vivid*, but *Superb* will be used throughout the book to refer to this yole.)

I investigated the adaptations and alterations that were made to Stroma yoles over the years, which included the changes in response to the installation of engines. To this end, four individual boats are studied in detail.

To broaden the setting, I also examined some of the contemporary boats on both sides of the Pentland Firth, in Orkney and in Caithness, and, having gathered all the information, considered the future of Stroma yoles.

The vast majority of information for this book was collected in the field. This involved talking to many different people, some of whom presently own Stroma yoles and still use them for pleasure or their livelihoods. There were people who were born and brought up on the island and knew about their forebears' lives; their daily work patterns and the struggles they encountered and overcame while living in the middle of the Pentland Firth. There were some people who had sailed in the yoles as well as maintained and repaired them. They had lived through the major transition from sailing to motorised yoles, which meant that the sails and oars were only occasionally used thereafter. Since no one lives on Stroma now, the fieldwork was mainly conducted on both sides of the Pentland Firth. A visit to Stroma itself provided an historical, social, archaeological and working context for the particular yoles studied.

As a research tool, oral testimonies of seven interviewees were recorded on tape. The transcripts will hopefully provide invaluable material for archives and for future research. Many other people supplied information and suggested other people to be interviewed. There were some disagreements among the interviewees over the construction details of the Stroma yoles; not surprisingly, as the last one was built in 1913. There is, however, substantial agreement on most of the details remembered. This is testimony to the extent to which the tradition of Stroma yole building permeated island life on Stroma and indeed the lives of those people who lived in Orkney and in Caithness.

The Wick Heritage Centre, the Last House Museum in John O'Groats and The Northlands Viking Centre in Auckengill were valuable sources of information. I also travelled around different harbours and their hinterlands in Orkney and Caithness in search of Stroma yoles taking many photographs in the process, some of which are reproduced in this book.

Background,
use and environment
of Stroma yoles

The island of Stroma

The Viking name for the island of Stroma (plate 2) was Straumey, meaning 'island in the stream', because of the fast flowing currents of 10 knots which flow past it between the Atlantic Ocean to the west and the North Sea to the east. The island of Stroma lies at a longitude of 3 degrees and 7 minutes west and at a latitude of 58 degrees and 41 minutes north. The island is part of Scotland and is situated 300 miles to the west of Norway. The body of water in which Stroma is situated is the Pentland Firth, which lies between the region of Caithness on the mainland of Scotland and the Orkney Islands to the north (figure 1). Stroma is one-and-a-half miles across the Inner Sound from Huna, or two miles from John O'Groats, and is part of the parish of Canisbay in Caithness. The nearest islands to Stroma belong to Orkney and are Swona, two miles to the north east, and the Pentland Skerries, five miles east of Stroma. Figure 2 gives a detailed map of Stroma showing the houses that people used to own, the names of the goes or creeks, the lochs on the island and the locations of the two piers and two sail sheds.

In Sir John Sinclair's *First Statistical Account of Scotland*

(1791-1798), the census of 1791 records that the population of Stroma was 170. In 1861 it was 291, and in 1881 it had risen to 341. Quite a number of people left Stroma during the 1920s because of the depression in Britain after the First World War. Most people, however, left during the 1950s. Many had been away during the Second World War and although they had been contented on the island they had seen a better, less harsh way of life elsewhere. There was certainly not much entertainment available on Stroma. A.J. Sutherland and A.M. Sutherland wrote:

In the early 1950s a new harbour costing approximately £30,000 was built in the hope that with no more hauling of boats the people would be encouraged to stay on their beloved island. But the wages earned on the construction helped many to buy houses on the mainland and this, coupled with the fact that there was still no adequate landing place for their boats on the mainland side, led to further and eventually complete depopulation.

Although the last family left Stroma in 1962, some former islanders carried on fishing for a while in their familiar fishing grounds, based in Caithness. Today, the island is used by its present owner for grazing sheep and cattle.

Characteristics of the Stroma yole

You can only get a Stroma yole if it's come from Stroma....When they left Stroma they built a boat called the Marigold *which is along the road there. Somebody said it's definitely a Stroma yole because it was built by the Stromamen.... It's not....because it was built in Mey [on the mainland].*

The term 'yole' comes from the Norse 'golle' with the 'g' being pronounced soft like a 'y'. A yole is defined as 'a small double-ended open boat, full bodied, for carrying loads, sometimes described as a knorr. Its counterpart was the skiff. There is no connection between the Norse or Orkney yole and the English yawl - a yacht.'

A Stroma yole was a very wide, or beamy, double-ended wooden boat featuring a stem and a stern post, the latter of which was quite sharply raked. The *Ella* (plate 3), for example, built around 1872, has an overall length of 20 feet 2 inches, a keel length of 14 feet and a beam of 8 feet 8 inches. Stroma yoles had characteristically wide and deep-sided bilges. The *Hope*'s stern quarters (plate 4) just in front of the stern post are very full compared with those on, for example, a South Isles Orkney yole. The overall fullness of a Stroma yole's forward shoulders, bilges and stern quarters gives it extra lift and buoyancy, especially in rough seas.

Stroma yoles were clinker built with 11 or 12 overlapping strokes or planks on each side depending upon its size. Edge to edge carvel planked boats were never built on Stroma. One source said that originally the open yoles came in three different weights; one, two or three tons. A feature of the yoles was their two deadwood knees, visible from the outside of the boats as triangular pieces of wood with a slightly curved hypotenuse. They lie under the curved extremities of the garboard strokes, or sandstrokes, the first stroke on each side (plate 5). Having the deadwood knees and the garboard strokes in those particular positions made the boats very strong. Stroma yoles could also be identified from their fitted floors and frames lying against the inside of the planking or the skin (plate 6). The Stroma colours on the yoles were white on the outside of the hulls, red rubbing strips and green gunwales.

Origin of the Stroma yole

It all derived from the island of Stroma, there's no getting away fae that.

According to one source, the original design of the Stroma yole may have been based on the Scandinavian boats as far back as 1000 AD. Since then the design would have evolved rather than have been discovered at a set point in time. Indeed, the Norse influence in Orkney began in the 8th century and continued up until 1468/69, when the islands were pawned to James III, the

Scottish King. Life on Stroma during this time was probably heavily influenced by Norse settlers. In one of the Norse sagas, *Njal's Saga*, there are references to different Stroma Vikings, such as Arnljot and Erling, who stayed on Stroma around 1014 AD.

Many people would have had a hand in designing the Stroma yoles with the shape 'very much like the Viking boats, just shorter and broader in proportion.... The waterlines of the Viking ships are not much different from the underwater lines of the Stroma yoles.' (It has also been said, however, that the boats which resembled the Viking boats most closely were the Shetland sixareens and fourareens of the 18th century, and that the Stroma yoles were a very different design altogether.)

There are various stories that map the start of the building of the Stroma yoles. Not all of them agree concerning the people who were involved and the date at which different events occurred. One person said that a member of the Smith family, who was the great-grandson of Donald Smith, said to be the first boatbuilder in Stroma, told him that there was a wreck of a Norwegian boat on Stroma and the Stromamen kept all of its strokes, then built a boat using the lines of the Norwegian boat. This enabled the Stromamen's previous design to be improved upon, leading to the design of the present day Stroma yole. Donald Smith was said to be one of four famous boatbuilders on Stroma in the 19th and early 20th centuries with the other three being Donald Banks, George Simpson and Donald Smith Junior. One source said that there was no boatbuilding on Stroma before the Donald Banks era, which began around 1890, and that before this time the people on Stroma bought their boats from Orkney or Caithness.

The Duncan boatyard was set up around 300 years ago in Burwick, South Ronaldsay, by two people, a Duncan and a Horne. James Miller said: 'There is a tradition that one of the Duncans taught the Stroma yole builders their craft in the early nineteenth century.' It was also said that a Duncan there built dinghies rather than yoles. Another source further explained:

It was a forebear of the Duncans, a John Duncan belonging to this parish [South Ronaldsay]*that was the boatbuilder and he worked*

8

down at Burwick Bay and built there. Donald Smith from Stroma was a young man who came across and served the winter with Duncan down here. When winter was past he went to Stroma and set up the first boat.

Houston relates that around 1845, two people called Banks and Smith from Stroma learned boatbuilding at the Duncan boatyard in Burwick, while another person said that George Simpson was also taught the boatbuilding trade on Orkney, then went back to Stroma and started building boats in 1865. Yet another said that Stroma yoles were being built on Stroma even before the Duncans started building boats.

The origin of the Stroma yole may also lie with the Stromamen themselves. Before the 1800s the yoles which were rowed at this time were used to pilot ships through the Pentland Firth. George Simpson and Donald Banks would have inherited their boatbuilding skills from their forebears, and with each generation of boatbuilders helping with the fishing during the summer time, the design of the yoles, 'came out of their heads. [They] just used their heads when they're sailing at the fishing. What can you do with this boat maybe, if [it] was not lying to the wind properly? Sheer experience.'

Uses of Stroma yoles

[The fishermen] *had an understanding of the tides that was almost uncanny. Knew exactly where they could go at any time to fish.*

The crofter/fisher community on Stroma was very interdependent, but the crewing of the fishing boats was nearly always family orientated. When a newly-built Stroma yole was used for the fishing it contained 16 shares. With a crew of normally four people, those who had bought the boat had four shares each. Fishing took place all around the Pentland Firth and was dictated by the tides. The fishermen worked with creels, which was mainly a summer activity, hand lines, herring nets and great-lines, the latter of which were mostly used in the winter time. Hand lines without any bait on the

9

hooks were mainly used for getting cod, so there was very little preparation by the women, as would be the case in other fishing communities. Once back on Stroma both the men and the women would dry and salt the fish, as they had already been gutted before they came ashore. It was also the job of the women to make the herring nets and all of the warm clothing worn by the men out at sea, such as socks, long drawers or underwear, sou'westers, oilskins and the long leather thigh boots which were rubbed with goose fat to keep them soft and waterproof.

Lobster fishing was carried out to the east of Stroma at the Pentland Skerries (figure 1). The fishermen would start off half-way through the flood tide and once at the Skerries they would haul their creels by hand when it was slack water. The fishermen then returned on the ebb tide.

Since the Stromamen knew the tidal conditions in the Pentland Firth extremely well they piloted ships, such as ketches and barques, through the treacherous waters, in exchange for particular goods they wanted. The yoles were often lifted on to the decks of the ships while the journey was made. The Stromamen, however, had to be very careful about which ship they went out to pilot because sometimes they were captured by a man-o'-war and forced into service. Occasionally they were taken as far as North America before they were allowed to get off the ship and find a passage back, and even then they might not have been paid or given the goods for which they had bartered.

In order to transport animals between Stroma and the beach at Huna, the main landing spot on the mainland, a cattle boat called the *Bee*, otherwise known as 'the big boat', was especially built. It was slightly larger than most other Stroma yoles being about 24 feet overall. The cattle boat would have been beached and the animals walked on to it. According to one source, the boat was pulled on to one side using a rope attached to the top of the mast, so that the animals could embark more easily. Stronger floorboards were made for them to stand on with the animals facing across the boat. About five or six animals could be carried at one time. When horses were transported they had to be sedated first to prevent them from jumping out of the boat. This was done by giving them some tobacco to chew, or it was put in warm water for them to drink. If a horse was given too much, however, it was sick, or it lay down in the boat, making it difficult to get it out.

As well as cattle being transported in the boat it was also said that they were towed behind, swimming. The animals were taken by lorry from Huna to the different markets on the mainland. Wick, for example, had sales every Thursday. During the 19th century, the people of Stroma cut peats on the mainland during the months of May and June and transported them back to Stroma in their larger yoles. The *Bee* has recently been rebuilt and today she sails out of Avoch harbour on pleasure trips.

Any time there was a shipwreck on Stroma or nearby, the islanders left what they were doing and went as quickly as possible, often in their yoles, to salvage the ship for its supplies. They tried to get there before the police and excisemen did. An important prayer by a minister on Stroma might be: 'Oh Lord, if it be thy will to send us a wreck, send us a good one.' A rocket line to which was tied a breeches buoy was sometimes used to rescue people from wrecked ships.

Stromness regatta around 1900. (Courtesy of William Groat.)

The people of Stroma also used their boats for visiting friends in Orkney and Caithness and one person said that a great deal of intermarriage took place among them. During the mid-17th century, the people on Stroma were encouraged to attend the church in Canisbay. On Sundays in good weather they crossed the Inner Sound in their boats. Records from the early 1700s relating to the church say: '...The presbytery enquired into Stromay, an Island in the Sea, belonging to the said parish (Canisbay), and found they were much neglected by reason of the dangerous passage to that place, especially in winter...'

Before the First World War, the people on Stroma took part in sailing regattas, (although according to one source there was little time for these).

Models

According to a display in the Wick Heritage Centre, the sport of model yacht racing originated in the north of Scotland. Model yachts, some of them models of Stroma yoles, were built by the people of Stroma in the same way as the bigger working yoles. They were used mainly between the First and the Second World Wars in model sailing regattas in the wintertime, both on the lochs on the island and in Caithness. Among the models of

Model yacht regatta in Stroma. (Photograph in Last House Museum, John O' Groats.)

non-Stroma yoles featured in the Last House Museum in John O'Groats, is the model yacht *Eclipse*, built by William Bremner of Stroma, who was also the coastguard in charge on the island. In 1933, he won a cup for model yacht racing. The writing on the cup reads: 'Challenge Cup, presented by Miss Stroma Sinclair to the Stroma Island Model Yacht Club, 1925.' Also in the museum is the model yacht, *Kestrel*, built by the late Joe McCaughey of Stroma around 1933.

On display in the Wick Heritage Centre is a model of a Stroma yole called *Stroma*. Plate 7 shows a model of a Stroma yole called *Crest*. It was built by one of the interviewees, although not on Stroma. Features worth noting are its dipping lug sail with its tack attached to the head of the stem, the square loomed oar and the thole pins, the side decks and the frames inside the hull of the boat.

Built for the Pentland Firth

The Stroma yoles…were powerfully designed to suit the rough weather in the Pentland Firth; otherwise they couldn't have lived in it.

On the wall of the sail shed beside the South Haven on Stroma, was a weatherglass or barometer to help the islanders predict the weather. As an aid to navigation a compass was used, which was kept in a locker under the small aftermost thaft in the yoles when not in use. The compass was housed in a binnacle with a gimbal, allowing it to remain level despite the movement of the boat. Some of the Stromamen could also navigate by the swirls in the water and by its colour. The fishermen never wore lifejackets or lifebelts and most of them could not swim. But, as one source said: 'They were such expert seamen, it didn't matter to them what the weather was like.'

On the 1998 Admiralty Chart: *Scotland - North Coast, Cape Wrath to Pentland Firth including the Orkney Islands* area, 1954, the following warning is given concerning the Pentland Firth:

The Pentland Firth....has extremely strong and rapidly varying tidal   13 *streams, eddies and races....Spring rates of 12 knots occur and extreme rates of 16 knots have been reported....Mariners should ensure that a close watch is kept at all times on the course, speed and position of their vessels.*

There are many dangerous spots within the Pentland Firth, and it was given the title 'Hell's Mouth' by the master mariners in the days of sailing ships. The 'Bores O' Duncansby', for instance, is a line of broken white water which runs out from the mainland near Duncansby Head, when there are easterly swells and a flood tide going from west to east through the Firth. Also on the flood tide there are the 'Wells of Swona', located on the west side of the island of Swona, two miles to the north east of Stroma. On the ebb tide there is 'The Merry Men of Mey' - a line of white water which runs out from St John's Point on the mainland at the western entrance to the Pentland Firth. Just to the north of Stroma there is a whirlpool called 'The Swelkie', which even on a calm day can have mountainous seas. Concerning these dangers, as one source put it: 'The Stromamen knew these as they knew themselves. You'd never see them near them.' Nevertheless, as another person said:

A small yole can handle as big a swell as you put to it ...You're losing sight of land....25 to 30 feet [swell].... *"tattie pits" we call them, the swell going up and down constantly....Losing sight of boats near at hand.*

In order for the Stroma yoles to perform well in very bad conditions they had to be excellent sailers. Part of the secret, as mentioned above, was that the boatbuilders knew the exact qualities needed for the boats, as they went fishing themselves in the summer. The yoles were not built for speed. The speed was governed by their waterline length, which was quite short, which meant that they sailed at about six or seven knots. As shown in the lines drawing of the Stroma yole *Superb* (plate 23), a specific design feature of the sailing yoles was their very wide, deep bilges. The bilge strokes rose up at a very shallow gradient of one inch in every foot and this also helped to give the boats stability and extra buoyancy. The large open hull meant that they had a large carrying capacity for fishing gear and for fish. Buoyancy was also a particular feature of the full stern quarters of the yoles as these enabled the stern to lift, especially when they were running with a following sea. This meant that waves did not come over the stern, thereby keeping the crew, particularly the helmsman, from being drenched. Generally the larger Stroma yoles were able to withstand heavier seas than the smaller ones.

Due to the storms that often raged in the Firth, the Stroma yoles were built as lightweight as possible and not more than twenty-four feet in length because of the necessity of hauling them up and down the beaches. A boat was normally launched stern first with two or three people on either side putting their backs under the skin of the boat and their fingers under the clinker laps and lifting it down to the water. This was made easier by putting greased wood, rollers or seaweed under the keel to make it slide and also by having greenheart, a very hard and greasy wood, as the false keel underneath the main keel.

Before the 1900s, the crews all worked together to haul

The Stroma yole, the *Miller*, rigged like a herring drifter. Wick Heritage Centre.

boats manually back up the beaches when, for example, six to ten boats had to come ashore because of the tide. The boats were kept above the high tide mark during the flood tide because if they were leaning to one side and resting on a bilge keel, the water washed into the boats before they righted themselves and rose with the tide. The reason why none of the yoles has its rudder in place in plate 1, was that they had been removed before the boats were taken out of the water. Even while the yoles were moored by the pier their rudders were removed to prevent the pintles and gudgeons being worn down by the rudders waving in the swell. Anchors were not used at all, even when the crews were fishing in one spot.

At some point, block and tackle and hand-operated crab winches, which had two handles, were used on Stroma to make the hauling of boats easier. The winches were positioned at the head of the beaches (plate 8). A rope was tied on to the ring at the head of the boat, thus enabling it to be pulled a short distance out of the water until the hole in the bottom of the keel, about two feet back from the base of the stem post, was visible (plate 5).

16   The Goe of Netherton and the northern pier, Stroma.

A U-shaped bridle was then secured by a pin through this hole and was used to give more upward leverage when hauling the boat using the winch. Greased wood placed under the keel made this easier and was usually the job of a young boy or a woman. There was no hole in the after part of the keel and so the boats were moved manually down to the sea. The boats were not turned around first to be launched stem first as this required too much effort. On the beach in the Goe of Netherton, at the north east end of the island, a small bogey or trolley with wheels was used to help haul boats up the beach.

If the weather was bad, people sometimes had to get up during the night to haul the boats further up the beaches to safety. It was not only at the North and South Havens that the yoles were kept, but at different places around the island such as in goes and beside people's houses. One source said:

*Looking back, they could have make life a lot easier for themselves...
Always work, work, work, from the time you got up in the mornings
till you went to bed at night. My grandfather worked very hard; we had
no time for play when we were young. He would say to me, 'Is there
nothing you can be doing?'....You had to haul the boats to the sea.*

The registration of boats

In the north east of Scotland a registration system was introduced in 1869, which not only kept a check on the different boats in the area but also a record of ownership. The registration number of all the boats started with the letters 'WK' which stood for 'Wick', where they were registered. Boats only had to be registered if they were used for fishing with the intent of making a profit, so there may have been other boats on Stroma used for other purposes. When a boat was no longer used commercially it was de-registered. Several owners used old numbers that they took off boats that had sunk or had been condemned. New boats, however, still had to be registered. It was considered bad luck for the people on Stroma if their registration number added up to 13. This however, according to one source, was not the case on

Orkney or Shetland where the people 'were very fussy that the number added up to 13'.

A yellow line was sometimes painted under a sheer or top stroke of a Stroma yole, or under the name of the boat, showing that it belonged to the major shareholder. If this person died the line was changed to a blue one for a year and then was changed back to a yellow one by the new major shareholder. This feature, however, was not seen on any of the Stroma yoles viewed during the period of fieldwork.

Building techniques

Building locations

All islanders can build boats. That's something you got to do same as sucking your milk out of a bottle.

Boats were tremendously important for the people of Stroma, because their livelihoods depended upon vessels that were built to a very high standard. It was said that every man on Stroma knew how to build boats with the trained boatbuilders being able to build them a lot more quickly. The boatbuilders had a very good reputation and boats were built for people on Stroma, Swona, South Ronaldsay and in Caithness. Moreover, when some of George Simpson's family went to work with the herring fishing over on the west coast of Scotland, they towed some of their boats with them and sold them to people there before returning to Stroma. Apparently the boats were built all year round to enable the builders to make a living because their craft was not a lucrative one. (One person said, however, that the boats were built 'in the back end of the year' as the summer was considered too warm, and it was harder to work with green timber, as it would dry out more quickly.) George Simpson, along with a helper, would have built yoles over the winter, but much of the time he worked on his own. The yoles were built according to supply and demand and estimates vary between four weeks and three months to build one.

According to one interviewee:

There was always a boy willing to learn; a seven year apprenticeship. But by that time the builder would have had his apprentice build a boat entirely....Sometimes it would be better done, but as [for] his first boat he had instructions from the carpenter. When they leave they'll be able to stand on their feet.

George Simpson built boats with Donald Smith, who had a shed in the north east of Stroma near to the Goe of Netherton and the north pier (plate 9). The present owner of the island of Stroma said that the shed would have had a felt roof and big double doors at one end. Donald Banks, who in his lifetime built in excess of one hundred boats, had his boatbuilding shed in the southern part of the island. A boat was even built 'up in a barn loft at Stroma Mains [the main farm situated in the centre of the island]. They had to pull the gable down to get the boat out. It was the only shed which they had [which was not in use].'

When George Simpson and Donald Banks worked together on a boat they always worked on opposite sides of it and even then the two sides turned out symmetrical. (One source said, however, that one side of the boat would be slightly different from the other!) The last boat built on Stroma was the *Barbara* in 1913 (plate 10).

Sources of wood

Since there are no trees on Stroma the wood had to be brought over from Caithness. A timber merchant in Wick, D. Sutherland & Son, has been there for six generations. The trees would be cut there into planks of, for example, half an inch or five-eighths of an inch thickness using a power saw. Even though the bark was left on the sides of the boards this saved the Stromamen a lot of work. The planks were then sent to John O'Groats to be collected by the Stromamen, or they would go to Wick to collect them along with other stores they needed. The planks were transported back to the island in the yoles. If the quality of timber they received was not very good they returned the planks to the merchant and were given replacements. Apparently, the actual trees were sometimes transported to Stroma from the mainland, towed behind the boats in the water. One story mentioned how a relation of the Banks family could tell whether a tree trunk had dry rot inside it or not. He laid his pocket watch on one end of a trunk and then went to the other end and listened to see if he could hear it. If he could, the tree was composed of good wood; if he could not, the tree had dry rot.

New wood was used to build the yoles; oak for the backbone and larch for the planking. One person said that fir might have been used for the planking, or indeed any type of wood that was not full of knots. Timber such as greenheart was used for the false keels.

Tools and moulds

Several different tools were used to construct the yoles. In order to fashion the planks and the frames out of a tree trunk a pit saw or saw-dog was used. This was a long saw blade with a two-handed handle at each end. The trees were set up on trestles above a saw pit and one person would hold the top of the saw while the other person in the pit would hold the bottom. They worked together sawing the trees. The person who stood in the pit, showered with sawdust, was known as the underdog, while the person above was called the topdog. One source said: 'It's not uncommon to get the apprentice boy on to that. If he's a good boy he wanted to do everything.' There was a saw pit behind the boatbuilding shed which George Simpson used in the north east of the island, but this is now filled in (plate 9).

As well as pit saws, smaller saws were used such as the bow saw. This was a lightweight saw used for cutting curves, with the advantage that the frame could be swung through 360 degrees so that it did not get in the way. The other tool mainly used was the adze, or the 'eech' as it was called locally. The boatbuilders used this tool for shaping, for example, the four-inch scares or feather-edged scarfs that were put on the ends of two planks to join them together in an overlap.

Other tools used were axes, wood chisels and planes, such as the jack plane, which, according to one person, was 'a short boggy plane made in the shape of a boat'. Plate 11 shows a collection of planes, which were in use in Orkney in the 1900s. The grindstone shown in plate 12 was used in the northern boatbuilding shed for sharpening tools. It had been salvaged around 1850 from a schooner wrecked on the south west corner of Stroma. A claw hammer was used for driving and pulling nails together, with a piece of pipe for driving the roves on to the nails once they had been hammered through the landings of the strokes. It was common for a child to hold the bucking iron against the outside of the planking while a person riveted the nails inside by peening their heads over against the roves with a hammer. In order to hold a new stroke in the correct position on a boat while it was being fitted and attached to the previous stroke, toggles or clamps were used which had a wedge driven down between their two arms, as demonstrated in plate 13. (The particular handmade wooden tool shown in this photograph belonged to George Simpson on Stroma.)

As an aid to constructing the required form of hull the boatbuilders would have followed certain criteria. One source said that wooden half moulds were used, although most of the work would have been done by eye to get the optimum performance out of the boats. (Another person said, however, that no moulds were used to construct the yoles.)

A ruler or a measuring tape was used to get the correct sizes of the timbers and the overall dimensions of the boats. String was used to measure, for example, distances from the centre line out to the edges of the strokes, which further enabled the boats to be built symmetrically. It was also said that at some stage the Stroma boatbuilders probably used wooden half-models in constructing the yoles. But even with the aid of some temporary frames, no boat turned out exactly like another.

They were all similar, however; the differences being in the proportions and fullness in certain places.

Setting up the backbone

The length of a Stroma yole was sometimes given by the length of its keel, which did not include the stem and stern posts on each end. For example, a boat with an 18 foot keel was called an 18 foot yole, with the overall length being about 23 feet. The vast majority of yoles had an overall length of between 16 and 24 feet. The cost of a boat around the 1900s was one pound per foot of keel, so if a person asked for a boat with a particularly curved stem post he got a bigger boat than one with a more sharply-raked post. The main reason behind having a curved stem was that a person could jump out over it and on to the stones without getting his feet wet when the boats came into the beach. The curved stem also meant that the boat cut smoothly through the water, giving it a graceful look. The outer face of a yole's raked stern post was more or less straight. The depth of a boat was in proportion to its length and its beam; the bigger the boat the more draught it had.

Stroma yoles were built right side up with the backbone being set up first. The stem post was attached to the keel, which itself was between 9 and 12 inches deep, with a vertical half-lap joint. Both sides were riveted together. An apron about two inches thick was then placed behind the stem post. A deadwood knee was put beneath the apron and rested on the forward part of the keel. These were either spiked or nailed in place. This arrangement was also followed at the after end of the keel with the stern post, the apron and the deadwood knee. In some cases the apron behind the stem post did not extend any lower down than is shown in plate 14; if it did it would interfere with the yole's fine entry below the waterline, and it would then be seen from the outside, which it was not (plate 5). In other cases, however, the aprons may have come lower down behind the posts, with their widths narrowing as they went down. The size and shape of the aprons and the deadwood knees also depended

23

upon the size and the grain of the available wood.

Plate 14 shows the backbone set up on wooden blocks, although one person said that it could equally have been laid on the floor of the shed without anything under it. The keel of a yole was always straight, with no lead present in it to provide extra weight. When the keel was made, it was seemingly cut one inch less than the round number of feet required for superstitious reasons. No hog was put on top of the keel. As shown in plate 14, two pieces of wood called cross spalls were fitted together in a V-shape, with the bottom part of one of the arms being attached to the outside face of the top part of the stem and the stern posts. The tops of the cross spalls were attached to the roof of the shed and were designed to hold the stem and stern posts in position, so they did not move out of alignment during the construction process. This allowed the boatbuilder to work with the two posts, instead of having them work against the desired shape of the boat. The posts were initially made taller to accommodate the cross spalls above the level of the sheer strokes. After the boat was completed the size of the posts was reduced.

A false keel was put under the keel in order to protect it from wear and tear. The depth of the false keel on the *Hope* was measured at one and five-eighths inches. Later, thin iron straps were used to protect the underneath of the false keels.

Steaming the timber

The wood the boatbuilders used for the backbone, planking and frames was all seasoned first, which, in the case of oak, for example, made it harder to work with than green or unseasoned oak. Although most of the planking was not steamed, the planks that required tighter bends in them, for example, those around the stern quarters, were steamed. These planks and even the timber that was used for the gunwales were placed in a steam box, which relaxed their fibres and made the wood more pliable. A steam box would be 14 inches square and anything up to 20 feet long, or the length of the longest plank. This would have been the garboard stroke, which fitted either side of the keel and was normally fashioned out of one piece of timber, unlike the other strokes on the boat. If a steam box needed to be made bigger, some more wood was nailed on to the end of it. Both ends of the box were packed with pieces of cloth, which also went around the ends of all the planks. This kept the steam from escaping from the box and gave it maximum opportunity to have an effect on the wood. The length of time a plank needed to be steamed depended upon its thickness, but some pieces may have been steamed for up to an hour. Sometimes the timbers were taken out of the steam box in the evening and were shaped before being left to cool overnight. The plank would then be ready to be fitted to the boat first thing in the morning. As one source said:

It goes stiff the moment it cools. You must take it out of the steam box, with pieces of sacking around it or else you'll burn your hands, it's that hot. [A man] rushes out with it, gets it to the bench and the clamps and he sticks it in with a bend in it. When he bends it, he does so a good piece more than he needs so it'll maybe go back a bit.

Planks and frames

The builders did not have to force the planks much to acquire the shape of the Stroma yole. The shape that the wood flexed to, once it had been steamed, was used to design the boats. The planking was either half an inch or nine-sixteenths of an inch thick, with 11 or 12 planks used for each side of a yole. The widest part of a stroke was in the centre of the boat where it was about six inches wide. The boatbuilders put on two to three new strokes each day.

A 'check', or a rabbet line, was a rebate which ran along both sides of the keel, the stem and stern posts. The vertically standing garboard strokes, or sandstrokes, were the first strokes fastened to the backbone and they were always in single lengths. The lower edges of these strokes fitted into the rebate in the keel. After the garboard stroke, two or three planks were used to form the other strokes. The third plank of a stroke was the middle one

25

and was called the 'slot', because it slotted in between the other two which were called 'headings'. The exception was the ninth stroke where, in the midship area, the boat was at its widest. In this instance two slots were sometimes used. The number of planks making up a stroke also depended upon the quality of the timber, but strokes made up of a single length of timber were generally preferred.

The end of each stroke was tapered and went into the rebate, or was 'checked in'. The rebates differed in shape as they went higher up the stem and the stern posts and were designed so that the planks could not spring out. This also enabled the boat to maintain its shape. A feature that was noticed in the Stroma yole, *Superb*, was that the scares or scarf joints were staggered, going outwards in a V-shape in the central area of the boat. This was so they did not lie in a straight line running up the sides of the hull, forming lines of weakness within it.

In order to get the same stroke on both sides as identical as possible, the planks were cut in the same way, with the same varying chamfers or bevels going along their lengths to ensure the landings would be the same for the stroke above them. So, when a new plank was added, a one-inch bevel was put on the outside top edge of the previous plank, and another one-inch bevel on the inside bottom edge of the new plank. The bevels were washed out at the ends of the strokes so that they fitted together, in the thickness of a single plank, into the stem and stern post rabbet. This enabled the clinker planking to be watertight at the seams. The different bevel angles put on the strokes enabled the boatbuilders to control the angle at which they lay. In order to form the required shallow gradient of the bilge areas of the Stroma yole, a rule of thumb was used whereby for every one inch that the strokes rose up, the bilges widened outwards one foot. This occurred in the area roughly between stroke numbers three and seven (plate 6). One source said that a mixture of linseed oil and green paint was spread over the landings in order to show up any undulations so that they could be planed down flat.

Half of the planking was built up before the floors and the lower frames were installed and then the rest of the planking was put on before the upper frames were added. As shown in plate 6, the fitted floors were made from natural tree crooks and went across the keel and were joined to the fitted frames going to the top of the sheer stroke. The fitted frames were themselves cut from the branches of trees, as these were far stronger than frame pieces scarfed together. Fitted frames made the hull far more rigid than would be the case if steamed frames had been laid in their place. The floors were located at every second frame with the majority of their wood coming below the level of the second stroke. The arms of the floors, or lower frames, extended up to about the fourth or fifth stroke, or as far as the natural crooks would allow, where they were then scarfed to the next part of the frame above them. The frames were located about one foot apart along the length of the hull, with the intermediate frames in between the floors starting on the garboard stroke and going up to the top of the sheer stroke.

Fitting the floors and the long curved frames to the hull was very time-consuming, as the bevel angle of each stroke had to be transferred to their outside faces. A breasthook or hunnispott, which was a shaped, triangular piece of oak, was fitted just behind the stem post, above the apron, and was attached to each sheer stroke. A breasthook was also placed in the same position beside the stern post. These provided extra strength for the top strokes of a yole.

Accessories

In order to bail the boats when they were at sea, tin pans or wooden scoops called owsers were originally used. Plate 6 shows that small pieces of wood were placed between the floors and the keel with a gap left on either side of the pieces of wood in order to let water drain to the deepest part of the boat, which allowed for easier bailing. Later, the Stromamen used a hand pump: 'A pipe and a non-return valve on the bottom and a plunger with a non-return valve on it.' When asked whether or not there was a drainage hole in the bottom of the Stroma yoles, one source said: 'A sea cock? No, there wouldn't be an awful lot of water in them

27

anyway, they'd just tip her up.' This was contradicted by another person who said that in the Stroma yole, the *Evelyn*, which he used to own, there was a drainage hole in which he put a cork from a bottle, on top of which he put a lead patch with a brass screw fitting over it to help keep the water out. The cork swelled up and kept the boat from leaking while in the water. The use of this type of fitting, allowing drainage of water from the boat when pulled up on the beach, lasted for ninety years. The owner of the *Kelvin Star* used to construct a 'nile plug' or bung for the drainage hole as follows:

I always use a brush. My brush is getting shorter and shorter, [I] *cut a stump from the brush every year.... I put a drop of anti-fouling round it or tar or bitumen.* [The nile plug is situated] *right in the bottom plank, starboard side aft.*

Fastenings

Swedish galvanised iron nails, which were soft and therefore good for clenching, were used as fastenings for the yoles, with the nails being purchased from the ironmongers in Wick. The holes for the nails were pre-drilled using a small auger. Iron nails were used, for example, for assembling the backbone and for attaching the planks to it. Large square galvanised nails called dumps, one-and-a-half feet long, were driven through the floors into the keel. While rivets were used to hold the strokes and the frames together, the proportion of rivets to clench nails used to fasten the laps of the strokes depended upon the preference of each boatbuilder. The fastenings were positioned at five- or six-inch intervals in between the frames.

During the late 1920s or 1930s, the boatbuilders changed to using copper nails because they could not get hold of the iron from Sweden. One person said:

[The Stromamen] *were never pleased with the copper nails. You had to be very, very careful with your clenching or they bent. Then with any stress on the boat they would stretch and straighten up, causing the boat to leak.*

When riveting copper nails, any remaining part of the nail which stuck out too far beyond the rove was clipped off so that only the copper right beside the rove was peened over, thereby hardening the copper against the rove, causing it to bite into the wood. The copper nails were very expensive for the Stromamen to buy. (According to another source, copper nails first came in the 1930s and 1940s, but they were never used on Stroma because all the boatbuilding was finished by then.)

Caulking, painting and tarring

A caulking material was put between the landings of the strokes to act as a barrier to stop water seeping into the boat. This material was described differently by some sources. It was called 'blair', which could be very finely cut sheep's wool mixed with Stockholm or Archangel tar. Horsehair was an alternative to sheep's wool. Concerning the material used one person said:

The old men call it 'pye'; a mixture of stuor and tar. The stuor....might almost be a mystery because the stuor was a ghost in ancient days. He came down now and again and did awful things. But he made the boats tight and you didn't see it. Stuor is dust, the dust off the cereals, it might be barley or grain....it's actually the pollen off the flower on the stem or the stalk....You can't get it on the market, the stuor, but that's what the Stromamen used....Stuor....It's Viking, ancient Norse, nothing to do with the spoken language in Norway today.

The 'stuor' referred to here was taken from the mill on Stroma and mixed with the Archangel tar to become blair. When the boatbuilders came to remove an old stroke on a yole the blair came off easily, just like a strip of paper. The blair did not go hard like coal tar and it formed into a thin strip through the course of time. It had the advantage of being kept tight against the landings by the rivets.

On the outside of the Stroma yoles, white lead paint was applied, which included lead and linseed oil mixed together. It helped to preserve the wood and killed any fungus growing on   29 it. The paint, however, was later banned because if it entered the bloodstream through a cut, for example, it caused blood poisoning. One source said that since the boats were hauled up on the beach regularly it was not necessary to put the red anti-fouling paint on them beneath the waterline, because the fungus was not given a chance to grow. It was only later, when the harbour was enclosed in the early 1950s and the boats were kept in the water more, that anti-fouling paint was used more extensively. This explains why some of the yoles painted with Stroma colours now have a red hull under the waterline, as they are kept in a tidal harbour for most of the year.

On the insides of the yoles, heated black coal tar was spread over all the bare wood. The builders produced coal tar by heating up coal in an oven and letting the tar run off. Coal tar was used because it contained oil which penetrated the wood, helping to preserve it. The Stroma yoles were 'very particularly looked after', in that they were tarred every year in the spring. At this time their outsides were also painted; first an undercoat, then a gloss coat. It depended upon how much profit a family made as to whether they could afford to paint their boat at times. The boats were also washed if they looked dirty. One person said that one share of the money made by a boat's shareholders went towards its upkeep.

Thafts and floorboards

There were mostly four thafts, or seats, in the smaller Stroma yoles, with five in the larger ones. As well as providing sitting places they helped a boat keep its shape and gave it extra strength. In a larger boat, like the one shown beside the pier in plate 1, the foremost thaft was positioned just below the height of the breasthook. It doubled up as a small foredeck and supported the foremast. The middle thaft in the boat also supported a mast. In between these two thafts lay another one. There were two thafts behind the middle one. The one in front of the stern post was for the helmsman. The rowers sat on the second and third thafts with the thole pins for the oars being positioned on the gunwales slightly aft of each thaft.

The thafts were bolted on to warings, or stringers, which were attached to the frames. The warings were three by two inches in cross section and ran along both sides of the hull about the level of the second or third stroke from the top of the boat. There was also a waring along each side of the hull supporting the floorboards or tulfars (plate 6), composed of five sections. These sections were removable to allow easy bailing. They kept people from standing on and damaging the skin in the bottom of the boat and kept their feet dry if there was water there. The only example of an open yole that was found with floorboards in view was the *Ella*, shown in plate 3.

Oars

A yole's oars were about the same length as its keel and each boat was normally given two pairs and a spare one. If a yole was very small it only had space for operating one pair of oars. There was always a person on each oar. Near the top of an oar there was a square-sectioned loom about two feet long, and it was this area that rested on the gunwale. The oar lay just behind a rectangular wooden or metal thole pin, attached to it via a humbliband or a piece of rope which kept the oar in place. The thole pins were covered with leather to prevent wear and tear on the oars; they acted as a lever to pull the oar against whilst rowing. There were also grooves in the tops of the thole pins used for hauling fishing lines. This additional usage of thole pins meant that they were called tomeboys.

The square-sectioned looms meant that the oars were non-feathering, and it was not possible to turn them to a horizontal position. The oars were typically made from spruce or Scots fir and had a spring in them when pulled through the water. This meant that not as much effort was required to row. Even if the Stromamen were sailing they still carried the oars aboard in case they had to use them.

Masts and sailing rigs

For them, going to sea was as natural as a bird flying.

There were mast and sail sheds located near the south and north piers on Stroma (plate 8). As is still seen in the south shed, the Stromamen kept their masts above the wooden beams with a number locating each yole's sailing rig (plate 15). In the north shed, the numbering system consisted of carved Roman numerals on the wooden beams. There were also iron pegs for hanging accessories. The masts of the yoles were made from spruce, Oregon pine or Douglas fir, known for having a straight grain. A yole's foremast was one to two feet longer than the length of the keel. The main mast was slightly shorter than the foremast, but again longer than the keel. A mast was always designed so that it could fit inside a boat. The bottom part of a mast was square in cross section, with a square hole in the mast step to receive it. This feature prevented the mast from rotating when upright. There were holes in the after sides of the thafts for the masts to stand in, with iron brackets fitted to the thafts through which a wooden wedge went to hold the masts in place.

The chandlers in Wick supplied the canvas for the sails of the Stroma yoles. One person said that the Stroma yoles were all spritsail rigged until the early 1900s, when the dipping lug sail was introduced, which the Stromamen preferred because it was more effective. However, it was also known that on the smaller boats with an overall length of between 18 and 20 feet, two spritsails and a jib sail were used. The tack of the jib sail was either secured to the head of the stem post or was attached to the end of a bowsprit. There was a ring on one side of the stem head through which the bowsprit lay. On most of the larger boats, up to 24 feet, a dipping lug sail was used on the foremast, while on the after mast a standing lug sail was used. One source said that instead of using a jib sail along with the lug sails, the luff of the dipping lug sail extended forward of the mast and was fastened via the tack to the head of the stem post.

While a feature of the spritsail yoles was the speed with which they could change tack, the dipping lug sails were bigger sails with a greater spread of canvas. One person explained how to put up a mast and hoist a dipping lug sail.

First set and fix the mast in the proper place, in the step down at the keel. Set her up, then your mast locks are your mast guides. Then put a fixed bar across and a wedge to hold it. Then your sail, the tack of the sail, at the bottom of the throat of the sail, that's fixed to your stem - and then when your mast yard and all's lying on the deck, you fix the traveller into the yard [plate 16]. *You have a block at the head of the mast and your rope from down at the bottom of the mast coming up through that block, and when you pull on the rope down through the block on the deck, your sail goes up* [plate 7].

The dipping lug sail was a very efficient pulling sail, but its disadvantage was that every time the boat changed tack it had to be lowered and the forward part of the yard changed over to the new leeward side of the mast. The halyard also acted as a shroud to counter the pull of the sail and was tied off on the windward side of the boat. Normally there were no standing stays or shrouds supporting the mast. When the sails were not being used there was a crutch in the after part of the boat on which the mast could rest at an angle, with its bottom resting in the mast step.

The Stroma yole, the *Diligent*. The mast and sails are being supported by a crutch.
(Photograph in the Last House Museum, John O' Groats.)

33

The rudder and tiller

The shape of the rudder on a Stroma yole (plate 4) was designed very specifically so that the helmsman had complete power over the boat, especially while sailing in big seas. The rudder was very full right to the top, unlike many modern rudders, which have a concave outer face on the top part. The fullness provided extra strength, as did the three iron brackets that curved around the inner face of the rudder and continued across each side. (One source said that he had seen Norwegian boats in Kirkwall harbour whose rudders were made in the same style as the Stroma ones.) The iron fittings for the Stroma yoles were made at the blacksmith's smiddy in Huna.

Concerning the original open yoles (without engines), the upper fitting on the stern post for the rudder was a sliding pin which slotted into a hole in the topmost bracket on the rudder. The bottom fitting consisted of a pintle and a gudgeon with the former being mounted on the rudder. It can be seen in plate 4 that a small concave notch was put near the top of the inner face

Stroma fishermen on board a Stroma yole. (Photograph in the Last House Museum, John O' Groats.)

of the *Hope*'s rudder, which prevented the tiller from moving down the rudder blade. There was also a notch in the tiller on its underside where it crossed the top of the stern post so that it could be swung freely back and forth without hindrance. There was no fitting on the rudder to hold the tiller down, allowing the helmsman to lift it and clear the height of the washboard when he wanted to change tack quickly. Some of the helmsmen found, however, that they had to guard against pulling the tiller up too far in case it came off the top of the rudder and went into the sea. To prevent this from happening, a pin was put through the top of the rudder on some boats.

The bilge keels fitted at the turn of the bilges on the Stroma yoles were tapered strips of wood that were designed to prevent damage to the strokes when the boats were beaching.

Ballast

It was vital that the right quantity of ballast was used because, as one person put it, 'the difference is life or death to you'.

The amount of ballast placed in Stroma yoles depended upon the size of boat, and their design meant that they did not require very much. While one source said that some of the bigger yoles had up to a ton of ballast, another said that the weight of ballast would be about a quarter or a half ton, depending upon the strength of the wind at the time they set sail. The ballast consisted of round stones collected off the beach and put into fertiliser bags so that they could be moved around the boats easily depending upon how far they heeled over to one side. With the ballast contained in bags, this also meant no mess in the bottom of the boats and reduced wear to the planking. If there were other heavy items in the boats, they served instead. For example, when the Stromamen were out fishing they sometimes threw some of the stones over the side in exchange for the fish they caught.

When the boats came in to land the ballast was tipped on to the beach or into the water so that they were lighter to haul up the shore. The bags of stones or just the stones themselves were

35

then collected or retrieved at low tide. This information is backed up by one of the bye-laws on a sheet entitled, *Stroma south pier, bye-laws to regulate the traffic at this pier drawn up at a meeting of fishermen held in the school on 13th November, 1912.* The bye-law reads: 'All ballast being discharged be removed ten feet back - as soon as the boat is beached.'

Plate 1 Stroma yoles at the South Haven and pier, Stroma. (Courtesy of The Wick Society.)

Plate 2 The island of Stroma from Caithness.

Plate 3 The Stroma yole, *Ella*, Wick Heritage Centre.

Plate 4 A close view of the rudder and the iron fittings on the Stroma yole, *Hope*.

Plate 5 A view of the forward deadwood knee on the *Hope*. The hole in the keel for the U-shaped bridle can be seen, used for hauling the boat up the beach.

Plate 6 The wide bilges of the *Hope*. The long warings on which the floorboards rest lie along the bilges at the height of the seventh stroke on each side.

39

Plate 7 A Stroma yole model, *Crest*. Scarfskerry.

Plate 8 A hand-operated winch just above the beach at the Goe of Netherton, Stroma. Behind it is a mast and sail shed.

Plate 9 George Simpson's boatbuilding shed near the Goe of Netherton, Stroma. (The saw pit used to be on the near side of the back wall of the shed.)

Plate 10 The Stroma yole, *Barbara*. Keiss harbour.

41

Plate 11 A collection of planes used in Orkney around the 1900s.

Plate 12 A grindstone used for sharpening tools, Stroma.

Plate 13 A toggle or a clamp with a wedge driven down between its two arms in order to hold two strokes together.

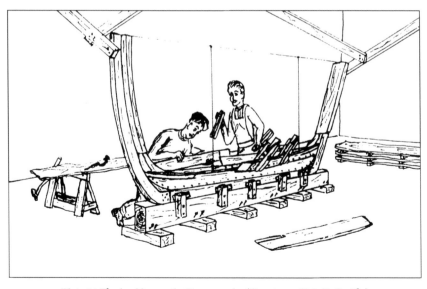

Plate 14 The backbone of a Stroma yole. (Courtesy of Mr D. Smith.)

Plate 15 Old masts still lying on the beams inside the mast and sail shed, near the South Haven, Stroma.

Plate 16 On the Stroma yole, *Evelyn*, the wooden wedge holding the mast in place can be seen. The metal traveller is lying a third of the way up the mast. The yard of the dipping lug sail is attached to it and is hoisted up the mast using the halyard. Keiss harbour.

Plate 17 The Stroma yole, *Dora*, John O' Groats.

Plate 18 The Stroma yole, *Kelvin Star*. Keiss harbour.

45

Plate 19 The 'Stroma type yole', *Rose*. John O' Groats harbour.
(A 'lapster kist' lies beneath the bow for the storage of live lobsters.)

Plate 20 A South Isles Orkney yole, *Gremsa*, under construction in Kirkwall (1999).

Plate 21 The Stroma yole, *Dreadnought*. Wick.

Plate 22 A view looking forward along the hull of the Stroma yole, *Superb*.

47

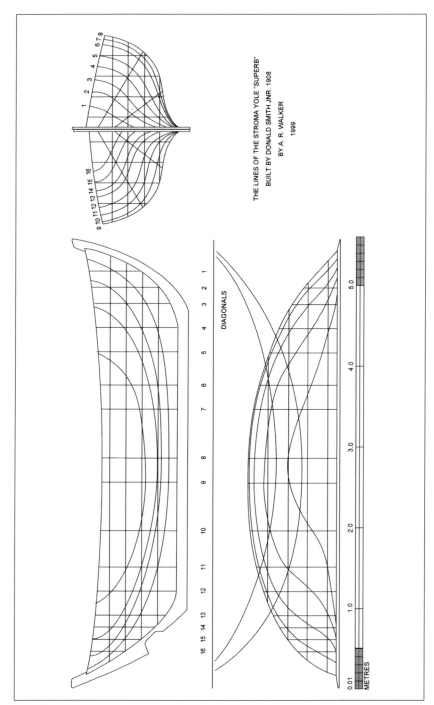

THE LINES OF THE STROMA YOLE 'SUPERB'
BUILT BY DONALD SMITH JNR. 1908
BY A. R. WALKER
1999

48

Plate 23 Lines drawings of the Stroma yole, *Superb*.

Adaptations made
to Stroma yoles

You couldn't make her anything better than what she is, you just could not. If you were going to make any attempt to do that, you'd just spoil the look of the boat altogether. She was a perfect model, that's what she was. (The owner of the *Hope's* response when asked which particular adaptations were made to improve his boat.)

Even though the people of Stroma saw their sailing yoles as superior to any other, small petrol/paraffin Kelvin engines were introduced into the Stroma yoles in 1912. They were started with petrol because of its low ignition point, but once the engine was going, the fuel supply was changed over to paraffin. At about this time, a number of other types of engine became available, made by different manufacturers such as Stewart Turner and Leyland Morris. The Brit engine was also used by the Stromamen, but it was not nearly as popular as the Kelvin engine.

It was commonly found that when engines were installed into the Stroma yoles the cheeks of the stern posts had to be widened where the propeller tube came out, otherwise the tubes broke the sides of the stern posts. Another option was to replace

49

the stern post with a wider one. This was in addition to cutting away part of the lower stern post to make room for the propeller shaft and the propeller so that they did not interfere with the rudder. The engine itself rested on oak beams which ran across some of the frames. This enabled its weight to be spread over a larger area, thus minimising the stresses on the hull.

When asked why an extra stroke was put on top of the original Stroma yoles, one person answered:

[When you] *put engines in the boats - and that was more weight for a start - some of the boats got lost with a lump of sea in the Bores O' Duncansby, and they heightened them an extra stroke because of things like that. It made a better boat. The engine dragged the stern down, that was the worst fault.*

The addition of an extra stroke, about nine inches in height, gave the yoles greater freeboard and meant that they were less likely to be swamped by the waves. This, however, often brought up the number of strokes on each side from 12 to 13, believed to be unlucky on Stroma. Perhaps in this case people just had to accept it, if it resulted in lives being saved at sea.

The practice of putting a form of decking into some of the bigger Stroma yoles occurred even before a near full decking was introduced with the installation of engines. Side decks were installed going right around the open yoles with a width of 16 to 18 inches. This particular arrangement was known even when there was an engine in a yole. The *Undaunted*, for example, built in 1906, was the first rowing and sailing yole to have side decks. The *Dora* (plate 17) shows the typical full decking arrangement with an engine installed. The yoles had a foredeck, a small after deck and side decks. The *Dora* is a 'Stroma type yole' (closely resembling a Stroma yole but not built on the island), built in 1935 in Mey, Caithness, by one of Banks family, along with a person called Moir. When decking was installed, a yole's thafts were either taken out and deck beams put in across the boat to support the decking, or the thafts were left in for the same purpose. The decking was mostly made from Douglas fir and kept the crew drier, the engine dry, and supplied the boat with the rigidity that the thafts had given.

As well as being able to stand on these decks, there were two main cockpit areas to stand in, the after one being for the helmsman. A fisherman could also stand in the after section of the box which covered the engine. When the boat was not in use a sliding cover went over this opening. There were, however, variations in yoles' decking arrangements according to when engines were installed. In order to help deflect spray, washboards were fitted which ran around the outside of the decking, nailed to the gunwales.

Engines provided enough weight in the yoles to offset the need to carry much extra ballast, if any at all. The speed of a motorised yole was about five to six knots, compared with the seven knots it could originally do under sail. Even though sails were not used with the engines they were still carried in the boats in case the engine broke down. An exception would be if the crew wanted to get home more quickly, and used both engine and sail. Some preferred to carry the dipping lug sail rather than the two spritsails because it took up less room in the boat.

The use of engines had a huge effect on the lives of the islanders, although 'many of the old men shook their heads at such an innovation'. Once a few people started using engines, however, everybody got them within a very short period of time. The fishermen's work was made much easier. It was now possible to motor in quite close around the shores to fish, even against the tide. But generally they still had to work according to the tide's ebb and flood. Although the engines enabled them to travel further afield, the Stromamen apparently did not travel greater distances.

Four case studies

The *Hope*

The *Hope* (plate 4) was built in 1906 as a sailing yole. When it changed owners in 1931, an engine was installed - an Ailsa Craig 6 horsepower engine, built in Glasgow and costing fifty-six pounds. At this time the boat had side decks all around the gunwales where creels were set. In 1931, the *Hope* had a winch which ran off the engine, situated on the forward starboard side, as an aid to hauling single creels. A small hatch was situated in the foredeck where a person could stand to haul the creels. A similar hatch was also a feature of the Stroma yole, the *Alpha*, built in 1901. This was the preferred location of the winch rather than hauling creels over the broadside of a boat. In order to avoid the edges of the strokes being damaged by the ropes, wooden battens were placed underneath the bottom edges of the strokes. It was not until after the Second World War that the *Hope* was heightened a stroke and fully decked over with the typical arrangement of two large open cockpits. The boat changed hands again in 1952, and the new owner installed a Volvo Penta engine.

The *Hope*.

It was noticed while photographing the *Hope* that a special iron bracket had been made to support the rudder in the absence of a part of the lower stern post, which had been cut away to make room for the propeller. The depth of the stern post above the propeller had also been increased so that the rudder did not interfere with it. The bottom fitting for the rudder was a pintle and gudgeon system, with the pintle on the middle bracket of the rudder and the gudgeon on the iron bracket which fitted around the keel, which came up and lay on the face of the stern post. This bracket was bolted through the keel in three places to hold it in place. An important feature of the bracket attached to the keel was that it extended out all the way to the corner of the rudder and was joined to its diagonal arm so that any lines in the water would not be caught between the bracket and the rudder face or become snagged on the propeller. The upper fitting on the stern post was a sliding pin which slotted into a hole in the topmost bracket on the rudder. It was this fitting which was used on the Stroma yoles before engines were installed. Similar rudder mountings can also be seen on the *Tern*, a Stroma yole built around 1900 by Donald Banks or George Simpson.

The *Evelyn*

The Stroma yole, the *Evelyn* (plate 16), built in 1901 by George Simpson, was later converted to motor and the hull heightened a stroke. The first engine was a 3.5 horsepower Kelvin, which propelled the boat very slowly and had no reverse gear. The boat had to be turned around the right way before the engine was started, and when the helmsman wanted to stop, the engine had to be turned off about 50 yards from the pier. This size of engine would have been too small for the bigger yoles but was used on the *Evelyn* because its overall length was only 18 feet 1 inch, with a keel length of 12 feet 6 inches. Later, the deck was replaced and the engine changed to a BMC 1.5, 39 horsepower one, which was slightly too big for the boat, but had the advantage of vastly increasing its speed.

The *Diligent*

The *Diligent* (see page 33), was built on Stroma in 1912 by George Simpson. Instead of being a double-ended boat it had a true counter, elliptic or fine stern. In the area of the Pentland Firth there were some other boats which had elliptic sterns. Two of these were the *Enterprise,* which was built on Stroma, and the *Hood,* built on Swona. According to the premise that Stroma yoles were understood as being double-ended boats, the *Diligent* could not be called a true Stroma yole, even though it was built on the island. The shape of the hull of the *Diligent* was described as 'barley bottomed' by one person, very like a clinker built barrel with no caulking in between the one inch-wide landings of the strokes. This made the *Diligent* very lively in the water.

The elliptic stern was said to have been copied from either the big schooners or the steam drifters seen by the Stromamen. The *Diligent* was originally built with an engine, a single cylinder 6.8 Kelvin. The elliptic stern meant that there was more space available in the boat than in a normal double-ender and the engine did not need to be fitted so far forward.

Having an elliptic stern meant that the stern post came up from the end of the keel and disappeared up inside the boat at the forward end of the stern, continuing up to just below the level of the deck. Stroke number six and upwards extended beyond the stern post and fashioned, without the use of frames, the elliptic stern. The shape of the hull from the fifth stroke down therefore fully resembled a normal double-ended Stroma yole. While one person said that the elliptic stern on the *Diligent* did not give the boat greater buoyancy aft, because most of the stern was situated above the waterline, the present owner said that the elliptic stern functioned in the same way as a seagull's tail feathers, in that it provided more lift. When the boat heeled over under sail it sailed more quickly because it had more length, including its elliptic stern, in the water. When the boat was running before the wind there was also a tendency in a big following sea for waves to break over the stern. In these conditions the boat had to 'sail on the quarter' (at a slight angle to the wind, not directly before it).

During the rebuilding of the *Diligent* between 1989 and 1992, a correction was made to its elliptic stern:

There was a mistake in the Diligent *when she was built and instead of the stern running with the sheer, the stern actually was built slightly crooked and this probably made her much wetter at the stern. But when we rebuilt her we straightened that out.*

The drooped stern explains why originally there was an unusually high boxed combing around the steering position. In order to maintain the shape and strengthen the redesigned elliptic stern so that its sheer line was a continuation of the sheer line of the rest of the boat, a fitted oak frame was put inside along with a compass frame, which went around the top of the planking just below the level of the decking. Another modification made to the original hull was that it was rebuilt slightly fuller in places to allow for the engine.

The boat is still licensed for fishing creels, which are hauled from the midship area of the boat. The owner has the option of operating using either a motor or a dipping lug sail and sometimes uses a jib sail with its tack being attached to the front of a 12-foot bowsprit. When the *Diligent* was first built, the oars were held in place by being tied to thole pins. The system now used comprises outer washboards and inner combing rails around the boat, with the tops of the upper frames, which themselves go down to the height of the tenth stroke, forming squared sections between the washboards and the combing rails. Wooden blocks, which contain rowlocks, can be put in any of the squared sections, to suit the desired rowing position. Additional equipment has been installed to make navigation easier; for example, a speed log, a depth sounder and a Global Positioning System.

The *Kelvin Star*

The *Kelvin Star* (plate 18) was built on Stroma around 1900 and weighed about 3 tons. It was only later in 1969, when it was

55

rebuilt, that a 13 horsepower Lister engine was installed, taking the weight of the boat up to 3.5 tons. At this time its head was heightened making it more proud, but no extra stroke was added. In 1993, the owner wanted to adapt the boat so that he could work it single-handedly. A bigger 20 horsepower Lister engine was installed as well as a wheelhouse, an hydraulic hauler and a shooting tray from which creels, tied together in fleets of 15, are shot off automatically while the boat is moving. Other modern equipment includes a Lowats LNS 350A, a Global Positioning System, a VHF radio and a sounder with a plotter. This is used to indicate what type of seabed is being fished.

If the engine of the *Kelvin Star* were to break down, a gaff rigged sail could be attached to the mast upon which the navigation lights and the aerial for the radio sit. A jib sail could also be used with an oar as a bowsprit. These types of sails have to be used as the boat cannot take a dipping lug sail because of the wheelhouse.

The owner compared the performance of the boat under engine power with a time he used a dipping lug sail in a strong wind:

The boat lay over in the water and she sailed faster than ever an engine would [have] *put her, and in hacky sort of sea conditions she took less water....She performed a lot better than she would under engine.*

The boat is now kept in Keiss harbour. When the tide ebbs the keel rests against the stones, so a steel shoe has been fitted to the keel coming about three inches up each side, which protects it from damage. Steel shoes, however, have not been fitted to the bilge keels since the boat rests against the harbour wall with tyres as fenders. The owner said that the alterations made to the boat in 1993 are reversible and that, if need be, it could be returned to how it was after being rebuilt in 1969.

The wider context

'Stroma type yoles'

Boatbuilders of Caithness learnt from the Stroma builders, and it was an enormous [number] *of Banks's that came out of Stroma that learnt the trade and spread through the north coast here, in Caithness. They were famed for their boats.*

The term 'Stroma type yoles' is used here for those boats which resemble Stroma yoles in form and construction but which were not built on the island. Apart from the Banks family, other people in Caithness built yoles with features which mirrored those of the Stroma yoles. It was the opinion of one source, however, that no one else could build the yoles in the same way as the Stromamen did.

The *Marigold*, a Stroma type yole, was built in Mey in Caithness. Its two deadwood knees were visible from the outside of the boat. The *Mizpah* was also a Stroma type yole, built in Edinburgh. In addition to its engine driven propeller, there was a vertical bracket mounted on to the starboard aft quarter for attaching an outboard motor. (This mounted bracket was also an adaptation made to the Nordfjordfaerings of western Norway.)

A boat called the *Rose* originated near the Moray Firth, but by the shape of its gunwales and bow it is very similar to a Stroma yole. The blocks into which the thole pins were mounted were a noteworthy feature of the boat, as these were held securely between the outer washboards and the inner combing rails (plate 19).

Stroma yoles' contemporaries

It was said of the Stroma yoles: 'You couldn't beat them in any direction.'

The Westray skiff, the North Isles yole and the South Isles yole were three examples of contemporary clinker built craft known within the Orkney Islands. Well-known boatbuilding families in the North Isles were the Omands on the island of Sanday and the Millers on Westray. In the South Isles, the Nicolsons and Sabistons were based on Flotta, the Duncans on Burray, and the Mackays on Fara (later in Finstown and Stromness). Three of the shipbuilding yards in Stromness were Baikie's, Copland's and Stanger's, the latter of which operated for about 100 years until 1928. Many crofts had a carpenter in the family and built their own boats.

The Orkney boats originated from Norway. They were transported to Orkney from around the 9th century in the form of timbers, prefabricated boats in kit form, or indeed whole boats. Later developments of these boats came mostly from within Orkney but also from mainland Scotland. The boats of Orkney were used mainly for transport between the different islands and played a part in the subsistence crofting economy rather than being used primarily for commercial fishing, as in Shetland. Other less frequent activities included shipwreck salvaging, lifesaving and the piloting of bigger ships.

The Westray, or North Isles, skiff, was known throughout the northern islands of Orkney. The overall length of the smaller skiffs with a dipping lug sail lay around 14 feet 9 inches, with the larger skiffs measuring around 19 feet 6 inches. The latter set a standing lug sail and a jib sail, the tack of which was extended out on a bowsprit. Compared with the North Isles yole, the Westray skiff, according to Mannering, was known to have a 'narrower hull form, with slacker bilges and finer ends (especially aft). It provided a more easily driven and weatherly hull, though it had less carrying capacity and was wetter.'

Compared with the South Isles yoles around the 1900s, those of the North Isles were wider and the stem and stern posts were more upright. Their frames were also more widely spaced. A yole with an overall length of 17 feet had a beam of about 7 feet 6 inches. The North Isles yoles were good sailers, due to their garboard strokes being attached almost vertically to their deep keels. While the smaller boats carried a dipping lug sail, the larger ones carried two standing lug sails, and a jib sail extended out over a bowsprit.

A typical South Isles yole had 10 or 11 strokes on each side compared with the 12 or 13 on a Stroma yole. Large South Isles yoles were about 18 to 20 feet in length with a beam of about 7 to 8.5 feet. They carried two unstayed spritsails with the masts being supported by the thafts. The foremast was slightly taller than the main mast and was about four-fifths the length of the yole. From the early 1900s, engines were fitted to the South Isles yoles, and after the 1960s the boats were mainly used for pleasure. Their sailing rig was also changed to a gunter mainsail and jib for racing.

Plate 20 shows the sailing South Isles yole, *Gremsa*, under construction in Kirkwall. Steamed frames were introduced in Orkney from the 1890s, after which both styles, steamed or fitted, were used. The limber holes beneath the floors on the *Gremsa* were a similar feature of the Stroma yoles. The shape of the North and the South Isles yoles was like a wedge compared with the Stroma yoles, which, like the *Barbara* (plate 10), were very beamy all along their length. This feature of the Stroma yoles was also evident in the lines drawings of the *Superb* (plate 23).

According to one source, the Stroma yoles had to be better than the Orkney ones because they were operating in worse sea conditions. The style, however, of some of the bigger Orkney yoles was very similar to Stroma ones and the Orkney yoles were also considered to be very good boats. There were a 59 few Orkney yoles found which had a very similar topside shape to the Stroma yoles. These were the *Primrose*, the *Kerri-Ann* and *Bessie*, all of which were built in Stromness.

Operating at the same time as the Stroma yoles were the open, double-ended herring boats which worked out of harbours along the coasts of Caithness, Aberdeenshire and east Sutherland during the 19th century, when it was said:

There came a boom in both the herring and white fish industry. Stroma men sailed as far away as Barra and Shetland in their 'firthies' and 'zulus'. Stroma became second port in Caithness for its catches.

According to Smylie, 'firthies' were also built on Stroma and 'resembled the Stroma pilot boats'.

While Mannering suggested that some of the herring boats' characteristics had Scandinavian origins, he also said: 'It seems likely that the herring boats' ancestry lay directly in the smaller open boats of the region's ancient, staple, line fisheries.'

Some people commented on the dangers of having a square stern or transom on a boat compared with the double-ended yoles of Stroma which cut through the water much more easily. One source said that when, for example, one is trying to go diagonally across the waves, with a square stern the diagonals of the boat are thrown up and down like an egg box. The occupants are thrown about much more and it is harder to keep control of the boat. It is like being on a horse when it rears its hind legs and bucks up and down.

One person said that in a following sea, when a square-sterned boat is running down a wave, the water catches the stern more than the head of the boat. This could push the stern around, putting the boat broadside into the breaking sea, which is very dangerous, especially in an open boat.

The future

I fully intend to have her trimmed up, not to be neglected. Try and save the breed.

The future preservation of Stroma yoles lies mainly with their individual owners and the time, money and effort they put into them. Small historical and conservation bodies, such as the Wick Society, which runs the Wick Heritage Centre, have taken a great interest in Stroma yoles. There are eight yoles there, some of which are on loan to the centre. Some no longer have their original Stroma names. A few of the yoles are under cover and form part of the displays. One is the *Rising Moon*, which was designed as a four-oared rowing yole; another is the *Miller*, which is currently rigged up like a herring drifter. This was the ferry for Eilean Nan Ron, an island off the north coast of Sutherland.

    Some of the yoles are at present in an open courtyard and it is the intention of the Wick Society to put them under cover in the future. In order to preserve these boats, they are tarred each year on the insides. Two of these are the *Ella* (plate 3) and *A*   61

Brighter Morn. One of the founder members of the Wick Society commented: 'I don't think any of them is really in a seaworthy condition just now, but they could all be made seaworthy, because no wooden boat is ever beyond redemption.'

The Stroma yole, *Boy William*, at the Wick Heritage Centre has been fibre-glassed on the outside in order to preserve its shape. Fibre-glassing a boat is much cheaper for the owner than replacing damaged or worn timbers. Other Stroma yoles in Caithness have also been fibre-glassed. One is the *Cormorant*, nicknamed 'The Grandfather' because of its age. It was built by Donald Smith at the northern end of the island, before or in the year 1887, when it was first registered. Some kind of relationship appears to exist between this boat and the Stroma type yole, the *Minnie*, which was nicknamed 'The Granny'. The *Minnie* was built around 1921, and has been subsequently fibre-glassed. Another fibre-glassed Stroma yole is the *Dreadnought*, photographed at the harbour in Wick (plate 21). It was built around 1901 by Donald Banks, as a cattle boat for the north end of the island. It was fibre-glassed because it was leaking, although the disadvantage of this is that any water getting into the boat cannot escape. It then lies between the fibreglass and the wood with the result that the timber rots away.

The Stroma yole *Superb* was 'built by Donald Smith Junior in 1908 for Willie Cusiter and John Rosie, both of South Parish, South Ronaldsay, who supplied the wood etc. at a cost of £6.10.' (Plate 22.) A lines drawing has been made of the *Superb* in order to record its shape and provide a plan for the building of future replicas, something the present owner would like to do (plate 23).

The owner would like to install a foredeck, a small after deck and side decks into the *Superb*. The boat used to have two spritsails with one mast situated in the bow and the other amidships. The owner's intention is to use the yole with a Bermudian sailing rig, and install an engine. The line marking the after face of the original stern post, above the cut-out for the propeller, can be seen. The extra stern post piece was added in order to take the inner face of the rudder away from the blades of a propeller. The keel and the lower stern post have been repaired, making it difficult to measure the length of the original keel. According to the owner, it used to be 13 feet in length. While the present keel is made from teak, the original was made from oak, and there was also a false keel of greenheart. The lines drawing shows that the overall length of the boat is 5 metres 56 cm, or 18 feet 3 inches. When a garboard stroke was replaced, the width of its planking lap was measured at one inch, reducing to three-quarters of an inch at each end.

Plate 22, showing the forward section of the *Superb*, indicates that the top two strokes of the 12 stroke yole are more recent than the rest, since they do not have any tar on them. When the yole's original sheer strokes were replaced, an extra, 12th, stroke was added on each side. The tops of the originally fitted frames now lie at the height of the 10th stroke and smaller fitted frames have been fitted to the top four strokes to hold them together. There were originally 17 frames made from red and white oak on each side of the yole, with floors fitted across the keel at every alternate frame. When the boat is made seaworthy, fitted floors will be installed at every frame position. The height of the stem and the stern posts will also be reduced by about three inches.

In order to integrate the Stroma yoles' design qualities into other boats, a boatbuilder who used to live in Scarfskerry, Caithness, built around seven clinker, double-ended yoles, their lines based on those of Stroma yoles. Two of these boats were 26 feet in length, roughly the same length as the largest Stroma yoles. According to the boatbuilder, there is 'nothing better than a Stroma yole to go and base any kind of boat on'. The yoles were built in virtually the same way as they were on Stroma. The differences were in some of the tools used and in modifications made to the boats to allow for an engine. To strengthen the backbone of the yoles, a hog was put on top of the keel. In addition, heavy engine bearers, which came up to the height of the bilge keels and were bolted through them, made the bottom section of the boats very strong. Wood of greater thickness was generally used, making the boats stronger and heavier.

As with the Stroma yoles, these boats had part of their deadwood knees showing from the outside. Steamed frames were quite often inserted instead of fitted frames because they were much quicker to install. Mastic was used as a caulking material in between the landings of the strokes. Furthermore, copper clench nails were used as fastenings for the boats, which, when given a quarter turn twist before they were installed, were less likely to come out. One of these new sailing yoles, using a dipping lug sail instead of an engine, would at today's market prices cost six thousand pounds. When asked about the types of modern adaptations people want on the yoles, the boatbuilder replied: 'People [may] want small cabins on them, but basically they just want them as original as possible.'

Potential further research

To enable a fuller picture of the building of Stroma yoles, a more thorough investigation would be required into the actual boats themselves, analysing the different construction techniques that were employed. For example, the dimensions and shapes of the individual timbers and their spatial relationships to each other could be recorded in order to give boatbuilders more information when they construct Stroma type yoles.

It would be interesting to study variations in hull form by looking at the Stroma yoles to see whether patterns emerged according to each boatbuilder's style. Consideration could be given as to whether or not the variations were in fact developments in boat design over the years. Further research could bring to light what happened to the other Stroma yoles built on the island. For instance, since Stroma yoles were sold to people on the west coast of Scotland, when George Simpson's family went there to work in the herring fishing industry, a search could be made for the yoles over in the west.

The boatbuilding sheds on Stroma could be excavated along with a detailed analysis made of the masts lying in the mast and sail sheds. A search could be made of the walls of the houses and caves on the island for graffiti, which depicts the building of the yoles and the maritime lives of the people. There may also be evidence on the island relating to previous types of boats used or built there, such as by the Picts, the Vikings and the people who lived on Stroma between the time of the Vikings and the 1800s, when Stroma yoles were known to pilot ships through the Pentland Firth. Search might also be made in archival manuscripts to confirm, for example, that timber and boats were imported to Stroma, possibly via Orkney, by the Norse people.

A comprehensive comparison could be made between the Stroma yole boatbuilding tradition and other types of boatbuilding traditions such as those of the herring boats of Caithness, the yoles of Orkney and Shetland and the Norse shipbuilding tradition. The extent to which these other traditions influenced the design and construction of the Stroma yoles could be usefully explored.

Another point worthy of research would be to discover what type of Norwegian boat the Stroma boatbuilders took the lines off to improve their own yoles. A similar design of contemporary boat might be found in Norway. In Caithness, an archival search might reveal information relating to the sale of timber and stores to the Stromamen and also the registration of the Stroma yoles in Wick in the early 20th century.

As a result of Captain J Washington's *Report on the loss of life and on the damage caused to fishing boats on the east coast of Scotland in the gale of 19th August 1848*, recommendations were put forward for improving the fishing industry. In practice, the 'recommendation that the Scottish fisherman should adopt decked designs like those in England were not acceptable to the Secretary to the Board of Fisheries in Scotland, much greater cost per vessel being the reason given'. Nevertheless, decks were gradually installed on the bigger working boats such as the luggers, which were used for herring fishing. It would be interesting to research whether the decking, which was put on some of the Stroma yoles before the installation of engines began in 1912, was the result of the recommendations made by the Washington report.

Source material

Much of the material in this book came from primary sources, and around fifty people were contacted. First hand information and impressions were invaluable, as very little has been written about the building of Stroma yoles. This in itself is very surprising, considering how much has been written about island life. Some people said that the research was being conducted too late, because so many of the people who built the Stroma yoles have passed away.

Although the people whose interviews were recorded on tape had not been involved with the building of the Stroma yoles, the last one being built in 1913, there was a great deal of expert knowledge in this field. Many other people were recommended for consultation but time constraints were against this. The credentials and knowledge of those interviewed were impressive:

William Mowatt MBE, South Ronaldsay. A blacksmith by trade, he had sailed and motored in his Stroma yole, the *Hope*, and had repaired several Stroma yoles.

Alex Annal, South Ronaldsay. At one time he had been an apprentice boatbuilder at the Duncan boatyard in Burray and had operated yoles built on Swona.

Iain Sutherland, Wick. A maritime historian and a founder member of the Wick Society, which founded the Wick Heritage Centre.

Malcolm Simpson, Thurso. His great-grandfather was George Simpson, one of the main boatbuilders on Stroma. Malcolm Simpson grew up on Stroma and used to own and repair the Stroma yole, the *Evelyn*.

George Gunn, John O' Groats. Mr Gunn and his family used to fish in the Pentland Firth with the Stroma yole, the *Hope*, before they sold it to William Mowatt. Mr Gunn also repaired boats.

Peter Sinclair, Keiss. A fisherman, he owns and operates the Stroma yole, the *Kelvin Star*. He has fished in the Pentland Firth and around the east coast of Caithness.

Peter Matheson, Scarfskerry. He has been building boats for the past 27 years, some of them based on the lines of Stroma yoles.

The following individuals also provided information:
Tony Blunden, Bob Clunas, Anthony Duncan, Robin Duncan,
Robert Dundas, John Dunnett, Frances Dunnett, Sidney
Foubister, Ben Green, William Groat, Mike Holgate, James
Magee, Sutherland Manson, James McCaughey, Alan Richard,
Brian Sinclair, Hugh Simpson, James Simpson, James Simpson -
owner of the island of Stroma, Don Smith, Len Wilson.

Glossary

Adze A tool, locally called an 'eech' in the north of Scotland, used for shaping timber.

Amidship The central portion of a boat looking fore and aft.

Apron The timber that lies along the inside face of the stem and stern post.

Backbone The stem post, keel and stern post of a boat.

Barque In the 18th century and later this term applied to a vessel with three or more masts. Each mast, apart from the foremast, which set fore and aft sails, was square-rigged.

Beam The width of a boat as its widest point.

Bermudian sailing rig A large fore and aft triangular main sail, the tack of which was set out on a long bowsprit.

Bevel A surface that meets another at an angle (except a right angle).

Bilge The part of a boat on which its hull would rest if the boat were on the ground.

Bilge keels Twin fins, very like those of a shark, that stick out at an angle underneath a boat.

Binnacle A container to house a vessel's compass.

Block and tackle A block is a pulley that has a sheave or roller set in between its two cheeks. (There are different kinds of blocks such as single or double.) The tackle is a means of gaining leverage and is where a single line is fed through blocks (usually two or more). The number of lines running between two blocks that support the load, determines the mechanical advantage and thereby the effort needed to raise the load.

Bowsprit A spar projecting out from the front of a vessel. A bowsprit allows sail to be set forward of a boat's stem and also provides an anchor point for the foremast stay.

Breeches buoy A lifebuoy in the shape of a ring, fitted with a pair of canvas breeches. It was used for life saving when a vessel ran aground. A line from the shore was fired to the ship, the 'rocket line', and secured to a mast. The breeches buoy, suspended by a sling, was then hauled back and forth along the taut line, between the ship and the shore. The crew member being rescued sat in the breeches buoy.

Broadside The side areas of a boat along its central portion.

Carvel A style of boatbuilding whereby each stroke lies edge to edge.

Clenching A method often used to attach two strokes together in the overlapping clinker style of boatbuilding. Once a nail is hammered through the laps of two strokes, the end of the nail is bent over at a right angle using an iron block called a bucking iron. This is done as the nail head is hit with a hammer.

Clinker A style of boatbuilding whereby the bottom part of a stroke lies on the outside of the stroke below it, and the top part of the stroke lies on the inside of the stroke above it.

Combing A board which, for example, runs around a vessel's steering position to deflect spray.

Crab winch A manually-operated winch with two handles used to haul boats up a beach or slipway.

Creel A lobster trap.

Crutch A vertical support with two short curved arms at the top. It is used to support the boom or the mast, or both, when not in use.

Deadwood knee The deadwood was the solid timber that was found in the bow and stern of a vessel, just above the keel, where the planking could not be accommodated due to the narrow lines of the boat.

Double-ended A boat that has a stem and a stern post and no rear transom.

Draught The depth of water that a vessel requires to float.

Ebb tide The retreating tide.

Exciseman An agent employed by the government to collect the excise tax on goods that were produced for the home market. It was also his job to prevent smuggling.

Faering A small open wooden boat from Norway.

Fifie A vessel originating in Fife that was used for catching fish such as herring during the 18th and 19th centuries.

Firthie The name given by the Stromamen to the Fifie fishing boats that came up from the Moray Firth.

Flood tide The rising tide.

Floor The section of a vessel's frame that extends from the keel to the bilge.

Frames The curved timbers that lie against the inside of a vessel's planking. Where the strokes are in clinker style the frames take account of the planking laps and are closely fitted to them. These are called 'fitted frames'.

Forward shoulders The section of a vessel just behind the stem post.

Fourareen A small open wooden fishing boat from Shetland with four oars and a single sail.

Freeboard The height of a vessel's hull above the waterline.

Gaff [rigged sail] The spar to which the top edge of a four-sided sail is laced. The sail is set fore and aft along the boat and is positioned on the after side of a mast.

Garboard stroke The first stroke on each side of a boat that is attached to the keel. Another name for the garboard stroke is the sandstroke.

Geo/Goe A long narrow cleft in coastal cliffs.

Gimbal The mounting for a vessel's compass consisting of two concentric metal rings. While one ring is fixed fore and aft along the line of the vessel, the other ring is fixed at right angles to it. The rings enable the compass to remain level despite the movement of the vessel in the water.

71

Great-line A long line with shorter lines attached to it at intervals. Each short line has a hook for catching fish. The whole line is laid on the seabed and after a while, hauled up. Great-lines were used for catching halibut, ling and cod.

Gudgeon The socket part of a pinned hinge. Two sockets, for example, are fitted to a vessel's stern post into which the pintles, attached to the rudder, slot.

Gunwale The top upward-facing surface along a vessel's side.

Half model A small wooden model, to scale, of the outside of half a vessel's hull.

Halyard A line used to hoist and lower a sail or flag.

Hand line A single line held vertically in the water. On the end of the line were two hooks for catching fish.

Head The bow section of a vessel.

Hog A timber lying along the top of a keel to strengthen the bottom of a vessel and reduce hogging. Hogging is the condition whereby the bow and stern of a vessel droop in relation to the midship section.

Hollow rising floor The section of a vessel's frame that has a slight hollow under it as it extends from the keel to the bilge.

Jib sail A triangular-shaped headsail that is set forward of the foremost mast on a vessel.

Keel The main central fore and aft timber of a vessel's construction that stretches from the stem post to the stern post.

Ketch A two-masted vessel that carries a jib sail, a main sail and a mizzen sail that is stepped forward of the rudder post.

Knot The unit of speed used by vessels at sea. One nautical mile is about one statute mile.

Landing The overlapping parts of two planks in a clinker built boat.

Leeward The side away from the wind; downwind.

Limber holes Small spaces above a vessel's keel, beneath the floors, to allow bilge water to drain to the deepest part of the hull so it can be bailed easily.

Lines drawing Drawing based on measurements taken from one half of a vessel's hull. A typical view shows the hull from the side, the bottom and either end.

Lines of a boat The shape of a boat's hull.

Loom The upper square section of an oar, just beneath its handle. When an oar is in use its loom rests on the gunwale of a boat.

Lug sail A sail with four sides set on an angled lug or yard. The lug sail is mainly used on small vessels. A dipping lug sail is one which, when a vessel changes tack, has to be lowered for the forward end of the lug, together with the tack of the sail, to be passed around the back of the mast to the new leeward side, as the vessel comes head to wind. With a standing lug sail the lower edge or foot of the sail is also laced down to a boom. This sail, unlike the dipping lug sail, does not have to be lowered when a vessel changes tack.

Luff The leading edge of a sail.

Man-o'-war A warship.

Pilot To guide a vessel through an unknown stretch of water avoiding the dangers.

Pintle The pin or bolt that forms the pivot of a hinge. A pintle is used in conjunction with a gudgeon.

Plank A piece of timber that runs around the side of a boat. More than one plank can be used to make up a stroke.

Port The left hand side of a boat.

Rake The angle of different parts of a vessel in relation to the perpendicular. For example, the degree of overhang of the bow and stern.

Riveting A method often used to attach two strokes together in the overlapping clinker style of boatbuilding. Once a nail is hammered through the laps of two strokes a rove is pushed onto the end of the nail so that it lies against the inside of the stroke. Most of the remaining end of the nail is then clipped off and the nail peened over or flattened against the rove so that the rove bites into the wood.

Rove A circular piece of metal with a circular hole in it.

Rubbing strip A narrow strip of wood running around the outside of the highest stroke on each side of a boat, to protect the boat's sides from, for example, other vessels and harbour walls.

Running The point of sail whereby the wind is behind a vessel, pushing it along.

73

Scarf joint A type of join between two pieces of planking whereby the ends of both planks are cut into a slant and glued together.

Schooner Customarily a large vessel carrying headsails and fore and aft sails on her two or more masts.

Share A portion of ownership in a boat.

Sheer stroke The name given to the topmost stroke on each side of a boat.

Shrouds Part of the standing rigging for a mast, supporting it side to side.

Sixareen A small open wooden fishing boat from Shetland with six oars and a single sail.

Skin The outer shell or planking of a boat.

Slack water The state of the tide when it is fully out or fully in.

Spritsail A fore and aft four-sided sail with a long spar or sprit stretching diagonally across the sail from its tack to its peak.

Starboard The right hand side of a boat.

Stays Part of the standing rigging for a mast, supporting it in a fore and aft direction.

Stem post The foremost timber of a vessel that rises from the forward end of the keel.

Stern post The aftermost timber of a vessel that rises from the after end of the keel.

Stern quarters The section of a vessel in front of the stern post.

Stroke A layer of timber going in between the stem and the stern posts that is used to build up the sides of a vessel.

Tack The lower forward corner of a sail. This term also denotes a change in a vessel's direction, for example, to 'sail on a new tack' or 'change tack'.

Tar Tar was derived from the distillation of turpentine obtained from pine wood.

Thaft A seat.

Thole pin A wooden or metal pin stuck into the gunwale of a boat to which an oar is secured.

Throat The upper foremost corner of a four-sided sail, set fore and aft.

Transom The plate that forms a vessel's stern piece.

Washboard A longitudinal timber projecting above the sides of a vessel to deflect sea spray.

Waterline The level at which a vessel floats in the water.

Windward The side closest to the wind; upwind.

Yard A wooden spar that crosses a mast diagonally or horizontally, from which a sail is hung.

Yole A small double-ended open boat.

Zulu A fishing vessel that originated in Lossiemouth in 1879. It featured the raked stern post of the Scaffie fishing boat and the straight stem of the Fifie.

Bibliography

Adkins, J. 1973. *The craft of sail.* (Walker and Company, New York.)

Allen, A. (Undated). *Orkney's Maritime Heritage.* (National Maritime Museum, London.)

Bowman, A. 1992. *Boats in Medieval Orkney.* (Unpublished M.Phil., Department of Archaeology, University of Durham.)

By authority of the Lords commissioners of the Admiralty, 1922. *Manual of seamanship. Vol. I.* (HMSO 1972-80, London.)

Cohen, S.B. 1973. *Oxford World Atlas.* (Great Britain.)

Davison, P. and Simpson, J. 1995. *The Glenans manual of sailing.* (David & Charles, Italy.)

Djupedal, K. 1986. The Nordfjordfaering of Western Norway: changes in an ancient small boat design in response to new technology. *The Mariner's Mirror, The International Journal of the Society for Nautical Research.* 72: 329-350 (The Society for Nautical Research 1911-, London.)

Fenton, A. 1987. *The Northern Isles: Orkney and Shetland.* (Donald, Edinburgh.)

Gibson, W.M. 1989. *The Herring Fishing. Stronsay Vol. I.* (B.P.P. Edinburgh; Kirkwall.)

Gibson, B. 1999. Orkney boats four centuries ago. Cormack, A.

and Cormack, A. (eds.), *The Orkney View. No.83 April / May,* 33-35. (Kirkwall.)

Green, K. 1997. *Archaeology an introduction: the History, Principles and Methods of Modern Archaeology. Third edition fully revised.* (Routledge, London.)

Helle, K. 1988. *The Orkneys in Norwegian History.* (A.s. Centraltrykkier, Bergen.)

Houston, A.L. 1996. *Lest we Forget the Parish of Canisbay.* (Congregational Board of Canisbay Parish Church, Inverness.)

Jackson, A. and Day, D. 1997. *Collins Complete Wood Workers Manual.* (Harper Collins, London.)

Kaland, S. 1987. *The Norse connection: Orkney - Norway, 800 - 1500. An exhibition to mark the 850th anniversary of St. Magnus Cathedral.* (Hordaland Regional Council, Bergen.)

Lipke, P. Spectre, P. Fuller, B.A.G. (eds.) 1993. *Boats, a Manual for their Documentation.* (American Association for State and Local History, Nashville, Tennessee.)

Mannering, J. (ed.) 1997. *The Chatham Dictionary of Inshore Craft: Traditional Working Vessels of the British Isles.* (Chatham Publishing, London.)

Marshall, M. 1987. *Fishing - the Coastal Tradition.* (London.)

Martin, C. 1998. *Scotland's Historic Shipwrecks.* (Historic Scotland, Edinburgh.)

McKee, E. 1997. *Working Boats of Britain, their Shape and Purpose.* (Conway Maritime Press, London.)

Miller, J. 1994. *A Wild and Open Sea, the Story of the Pentland Firth.* (The Orkney Press Ltd., Kirkwall.)

Osler, A. 1983. *The Shetland Boat, South Mainland and Fair Isle. Maritime Monographs and Reports, No. 58.* (Trustees of the National Maritime Museum, London.)

Pottinger, M. 1993. *Stroma.* Cormack, A. and Cormack, A. (eds.), *The Orkney View. No. 46 February/March,* 11-13. (The Orcadian Ltd., Kirkwall.)

Robertson, J.D.M. 1991. *An Orkney Anthology, the Selected Works of Ernest Walker Marwick. Vol.I* (Scottish Academic Press, Edinburgh.)

Smylie, M. 1999. *Traditional Fishing Boats of Britain and Ireland: Design, History and Evolution.* (Waterline Books, Shrewsbury.)

Thowsen, A. 1968. *En studie i vestnorsk trebat- og treskipsbygging.* (A

Study in West Norwegian Wooden Boat and Wooden Ship Building.) (*Sjofartshistorisk Arbok*. Seafaring Historical Yearbook. 7-71.)

Thowsen, A. 1969. *The Norwegian Export of Boats to Shetland and its Influence upon Shetland Boatbuilding and Usage.* (*Sjofartshistorisk Arbok.* 145-203.)

Watt, T. 1998. The Ness Yoal - Saved from Certain Death? (Djerw, U. and Haasum, S. (eds.), *Manniskor och batar i Norden.* Stockholm.)

White, E.W. 1957. *British Fishing - Boats and Coastal Craft, part I: Historical Survey.* (London.)

Young, D. (ed.) 1992 . *Stroma.* (North of Scotland Newspapers, Inverness.)

The register of sea fishing boats in Scotland - Wick registered. 1912-1914. (North Highland Archive, Wick Library.)

Leaflets

Aitken, M. *The Island of Stroma.*

Cassells, I. *The Raven Banner. A guide to Viking Caithness.* (Thurso.)

Dundas, R.G. *Stroma Island.*

Sutherland, I. *Wick Heritage Centre Guide.* (The Wick Society.)

Sutherland, A.J. & Sutherland, A.M. *The Last House in Scotland Museum.* (John O' Groats.)

Vikings. (Caithness Museum Service, Wick.)

Stroma south pier, bye-laws to regulate the traffic at this pier drawn up at a meeting of fishermen held in the school on 13th November 1912. (Last House Museum, John O' Groats.)

A brief history of Caithness maritime activity through archives. (North Highland Archive, Wick Library. June 1999.)